Nurturing Naasir & His Power to Share

Written By
Sedara Burson

www.SedaraBursonLPC.com

Marley:
Give & Live
Freely!
Sedara

ISBN: 978-0-9993464-3-3

Illustrations by Abira Das, Editor Marsha Burson, B.S., Ms. Ed.
Graphic Design by Remi Bryant of Remiz Art & Design

Dedication

I dedicate this book to the spirit of resilience and abundance. We have all been tested this past year and yet have come out stronger, more healthy and more connected. Despite the things that have been taken from us last year, continue to believe in abundance.

Give and live freely!

Amen
Ashe'
So It Is Done

Once upon a time there was a little boy named Naasir, who loved being generous.

He would share with his family.

He would share with his friends.

He would share with his neighbors.

It made him feel good to give to others. He never thought about if others shared with him, it didn't matter.

Naasir felt confused because he always shared with others and he had often shared with her.

He didn't understand why she would not share with him.

Later that day, Naasir went home and talked with his father about what happened.

Naasir thought about this and still felt confused. He asked his dad, "Does this mean I shouldn't share with her anymore? Should I stop sharing with people?"

His dad said, "Son, what does her decision have to do with your decision? You never shared because others shared with you before. You shared because you wanted to."

Naasir said, "You are right; it makes me feel good to give to others. I shouldn't stop being myself because someone did something different than I."

Golden Rule

His dad said, "When I was little, my mom told me about the Golden Rule, which was to treat others how you want to be treated. I encourage you to take it one step further."

Naasir asked, "How do I do that?" His dad said, "Well, it's kind of hard but you should try to treat people how you want to be treated despite how they treat you."

Platinum Rule

Naasir asked, "Well, what do you call that rule?" His dad said, "I call it the Platinum Rule!"

The next day Naasir went to school and sat next to his schoolmate who wouldn't share, as he always does. His mom packed him his favorite snacks that his friend loves, too.

He offered her one of his snacks and she looked surprised after how she treated him the day before. Naasir still felt good about sharing!

He talked to her about what happened, and she apologized for not sharing. She explained that sometimes lunch is the last meal she gets before she goes home.

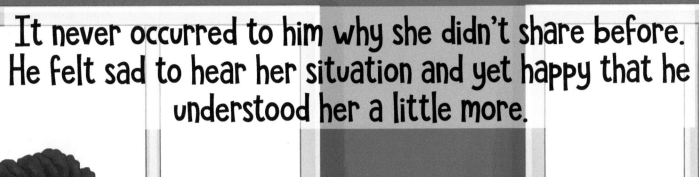

It never occurred to him why she didn't share before. He felt sad to hear her situation and yet happy that he understood her a little more.

Naasir decided in that moment that he will continue to do what feels good and not let what other people do change who he is.

Naasir told his dad all about his day when he got home. He told his dad, "it's important that I do what's right. Doing what others do can take me away from being me."

Naasir said, "I think I understand, Dad. No matter what others do or why, keep true to myself!"

About The Author

Sedara Burson is a daughter, mother, sister, aunt and counselor. She is personally and professionally interested in helping people of all ages understand how to become emotionally mature.

This book focuses on the importance of giving, remaining true to yourself and honoring your own core values. We take the Golden Rule up a notch and teach children about the Platinum Rule!

If you have not had a chance to read her first two books, definitely get your copies today. Master Maasai and His Power to Choose was written to help children learn how much power they have to stay strong within, even when things are changing around them and inside of them. Noble Nyela and Her Power to Create helps children understand their power to create the world they want through positive thinking and hard work.

Get all three at www.SedaraBursonLPC.com!

Other books to follow will address the importance of taking care of the environment and the importance of teaching others how to treat you.